Dean Sorenson   First Place for Jazz ™

Dear Student,

Welcome to *First Place for Jazz!* This book and related multimedia materials will introduce you to the basics of jazz through tunes that you can play and perform in a variety of settings.

Learning to play jazz requires hard work and dedication. You have taken an important step by coming here FIRST! Best wishes as you begin this journey.

Sincerely,

Dean Sorenson

Dean Sorenson

Interactive Practice—the key to Success!

Demonstration and play-along recordings of all the music and exercises in *First Place for Jazz* can be found in the *First Place for Jazz Interactive Practice Studio*. There, you can change the speed of the accompaniments and even create recordings of your playing. You can also download accompaniments for use on your media player. The *Interactive Practice Studio* is an ever-changing and ever-growing resource. Visit often to take advantage of additions to the *First Place for Jazz* curriculum.

To access your *Interactive Practice Studio*, download the software at www.kjos.com/ips. Follow the on-screen instructions and use the sixteen-digit code located on the inside back cover of this book to get started. For tech support, email: interactivestudio@kjos.com. IPS license will expire in 12 month~~~~~~~~~~~al is available for additional usage.

D1262105

 First Place for Jazz is available in SmartMusic.
To subscribe go to www.smartmusic.com.

ISBN-10: 0-8497-7107-2 • ISBN-13: 978-0-8497-7107-1

First Place for Jazz and **IPS INTERACTIVE Practice Studio** are trademarks of Kjos Music Press.

Jumpin' Jellybeans
Piano Spotlight

Use the recordings and other features included in the *First Place for Jazz Interactive Practice Studio*. See page 1 for more details.

Exercise A will help you practice the basic rhythm section groove from the solo section of *Jumpin' Jellybeans*. The bass clef doubles the bass line, and is included in case your director asks you to play it. On the recording, you will hear the treble clef part only.

Concert B♭

A

JAZZ THEORY **Chord symbols** are notated on top of the staff and define the chords that are used. The vertical arrangement of the different chord tones is called the chord **voicing**. More advanced jazz piano players create their own voicings from the chord symbols, but in *First Place for Jazz* all the chord voicings are provided for you.

Groove describes the chords and rhythm patterns that the rhythm section plays. It is often expressed in terms of style. For example, *Jumpin' Jellybeans* is in a rock groove. The groove usually stays pretty consistent throughout a chart, as it does in *Jumpin' Jellybeans*.

When you see the marking "As Is" in a part, it means that you should play the music as written in both hands. This is often done when the piano is doubling lines played in the ensemble. Make sure to follow the articulation markings carefully. The excerpt in Exercise B occurs several times in *Jumpin' Jellybeans*. Listen carefully to the recording and match it as closely as possible.

B

JAZZ THEORY The markings above the notes are **articulations**. These markings tell you to play a note long or short, with emphasis (accented), or without. The recording demonstrates these articulations.

The piano groove for *Jumpin' Jellybeans* changes slightly at bar 29 of the jazz ensemble chart. Exercise C will help you practice this new groove. Note the "As Is" marking toward the end of the exercise. Listen carefully to the recording and match it as closely as possible. On the recording, you will hear the treble clef part only, except in the "As Is" section.

C

☐ Check your progress on page 3 after each exercise. ➤

Concert B♭

LESSON 1 - Begin with Bass and Kick Drum

Listen as the bass and kick drum play. Focus on rhythm, tempo, and balance. Your director may ask you to play the bass clef part of your music from Lesson 2 if there is no bass player in the ensemble, or to reinforce the bass line. The piano bass clef part is identical to the bass part.

 Jumpin' Jellybeans is in a **rock** style. Rock styles use straight eighth notes, not swing eighth notes, and should have a driving and forward-moving feel.

LESSON 2 - Add Guitar, Piano, and Vibes

Play the exercise, focusing on rhythm, tempo, and balance. Omit the bass clef part unless your director asks you to play it. Listen carefully to the recording and match it as closely as possible.

Note: This exercise is not repeated on the recording.

 Guitar, piano, and vibes are **comping** instruments. Comping is a technique used to ac**comp**any or **comp**lement the parts played by the other members of the ensemble. It involves creating a rhythmically-appropriate part that follows the chord changes of the music.

LESSON 3 - Add Snare Drum, Cowbell, and Bongos

Play your part from Lesson 2, focusing on rhythm, tempo, and balance. Match the recording as closely as possible.

 Backbeats (beats 2 and 4 in ⁴⁄₄) are fundamental to the rhythmic drive of the rock groove. They are usually played on snare drum in rock styles.

LESSON 4 - Add Closed Hi-hat and Crash Cymbal - Complete Groove

Play your part from Lesson 2, focusing on rhythm, tempo, and balance. Match the recording as closely as possible.

 A cymbal crash is often played by the drummer at the beginning of each section of the piece, or when a section repeats. This is important to help **mark the form**, for performers and listeners.

Practice your part by using the **rhythm section practice track** for your instrument.

Concert B♭

B♭ Major Scale

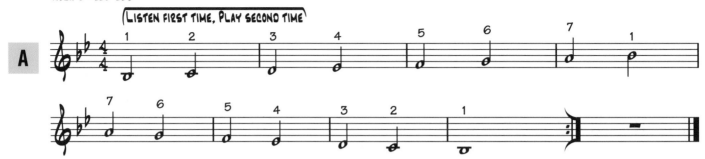

JAZZ THEORY *Jumpin' Jellybeans* uses the **B♭ major scale.** Numbers above the notes refer to the scale **degrees.** The first note is called the **first degree** or **tonic,** the second note is the **second degree,** and so on. When the scale is repeated in the next octave, the numbering system starts over again at 1.

B♭ Major Pitch Sets

After listening to and playing each Pitch Set as written, skip to **Improvisation Practice** and play a solo using only those scale degrees.

Use any scale degree. Write the scale degrees above the notes before you play.

B♭ Major Seventh Chord — B♭MA7

Write a B♭MA7 chord in the staff below.

Write half note chord tones for B♭MA7 as indicated in the staff below. There is no key signature, so don't forget to add accidentals. Play the chord tones to hear the relationships.

JAZZ THEORY In *Jumpin' Jellybeans*, the **major seventh chord** built on B♭ is used. The chord symbol is B♭MA7. Seventh chords are constructed of four notes. The bottom note is called the **root (R)**, the next note is the **third (3)**, the next note is the **fifth (5)**, and the top note is the **seventh (7)**. In major seventh chords, these **chord tones** correspond to the first, third, fifth, and seventh degrees of the major scale.

Accompaniment Grooves

Use this Accompaniment Groove for exercise **A** and **Improvisation Practice**.

Use this Accompaniment Groove for exercise **B** and **D**.

↑ Two-Measure Repeat Sign —
repeat the two previous measures.

Improvisation Practice

Improvisation Practice takes you through the solo section of *Jumpin' Jellybeans* two times. Even though the chords change, you can improvise over the entire solo section using pitches from the B♭ major scale.

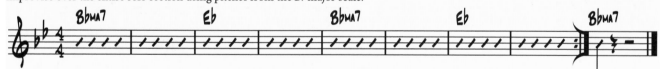

✓ Let's Check Progress

			Practiced		Mastered
Piano Spotlight	**A**				
	B				
	C				
Rhythm Sectional	**4**				

B♭ Major

				Practiced	Mastered
A	Play				
B1	As Written				
	Improv Practice				
B2	As Written				
	Improv Practice				
B3	As Written				
	Improv Practice				
B4	As Written				
	Improv Practice				
C	Write				
	Play				

Apply what you have learned from the Jazz Starters as you play the *Jumpin' Jellybeans* **Jazz Ensemble Chart** on pages 4 and 5 or **Lead Sheet** on page 50/51. ➡

Jumpin' Jellybeans

Dean Sorenson

*To practice soloing on this chart, use the solo section accompaniment groove recording in your *Interactive Practice Studio*. The written solo is played the first time through.

Quarterback Sneak
Piano Spotlight

Use the recordings and other features included in the *First Place for Jazz Interactive Practice Studio*. See page 1 for more details.

Concert B♭

Exercise A will help you practice the basic rhythm section groove for the solo section of *Quarterback Sneak*. The bass clef doubles the bass line, and is included in case your director asks you to play it. On the recording, you will hear the treble clef part only.

Whenever you see chord symbols in a part, you are free to create your own part instead of playing the written groove. If you choose to create your own part, make certain it is consistent with the style and harmony of the music.

Two-Measure Repeat Sign — repeat the two previous measures.

JAZZ THEORY Piano parts often use shorthand to notate repetitive music. The two-measure repeat sign used in bars 3 and 4 of Exercise A means you should play the same music from the previous two bars. When that marking is used over and over again, it means to play the same two bars over and over again.

Exercise B will help you practice several passages from the *Quarterback Sneak* jazz ensemble chart where you are to play "As Is." Practice this exercise until you can play it comfortably.

JAZZ THEORY The marking **As Is** is often used when music should be played exactly as written. This marking generally means that your part is the same as other parts in the ensemble.

Exercise C is taken from bars 31 through 34 of the *Quarterback Sneak* jazz ensemble chart and includes slight changes in the rhythm section groove. These changes help to create interest and to keep the music moving forward.

☐ Check your progress on page 7 after each exercise. ➤

Quarterback Sneak
Rhythm Sectional

LESSON 1 - Begin with Bass and Kick Drum

Listen as the bass and kick drum play. Focus on rhythm, tempo, and balance. Your director may ask you to play the bass line of your piano part from Lesson 2 if there is no bass player in the ensemble, or to reinforce the bass part. The piano bass line is identical to the bass part.

 Quarterback Sneak is in a **bossa nova** style, commonly notated as **bossa.** Bossa styles use straight eighth notes, not swing eighth notes, and should have a very relaxed but rhythmic feel to them.

LESSON 2 - Add Guitar, Piano, and Vibes

Play the exercise, focusing on rhythm, tempo, and balance. Omit the bass clef part unless your director asks you to play it. Listen carefully to the recording and match it as closely as possible.

Note: This exercise is not repeated on the recording.

 Guitar, piano, and vibes are **comping** instruments. During solos it is preferred that only one instrument comp at a time, or the texture of the rhythm section can become muddy. Piano, guitar, and vibes should decide in advance which instrument is going to comp behind the different soloists.

LESSON 3 - Add Cross-Stick, Claves, and Congas

Play your part from Lesson 2, focusing on rhythm, tempo, and balance. Match the recording as closely as possible.

 The **clave**, usually a syncopated two-bar rhythm pattern, is a central element in many Latin styles. The clave pattern may change slightly depending on the type of Latin music being performed, but this rhythm permeates the entire piece. Note that the clave *rhythm* should not be confused with the *percussion instrument* called claves.

LESSON 4 - Add Closed Hi-hat and Crash Cymbal - Complete Groove

Play your part from Lesson 2, focusing on rhythm, tempo, and balance. Match the recording as closely as possible.

 Along with the clave rhythm, listen for the running eighth notes in the closed hi-hat and congas. The constant motion of the eighth notes will provide a steady pattern that supports the groove.

Practice your part by using the **rhythm section practice track** for your instrument.

B♭ Mixolydian Scale

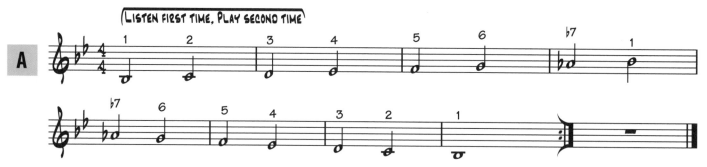

JAZZ THEORY *Quarterback Sneak* uses the **B♭ Mixolydian scale**. The Mixolydian scale is the same as the major scale except the seventh degree is lowered one half step. This is why the seventh degree of the Mixolydian scale is labeled as ♭**7**. If you can play the B♭ major scale, all you have to do is lower the seventh to play the B♭ Mixolydian scale.

B♭ Mixolydian Pitch Sets

After listening to and playing each Pitch Set as written, skip to **Improvisation Practice** and play a solo using only those scale degrees.

Use any scale degree. Write the scale degrees above the notes before you play.

B♭ Dominant Seventh Chord — B♭7

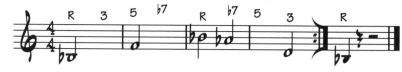

JAZZ THEORY In *Quarterback Sneak*, the **dominant seventh chord** built on B♭ is used. The chord symbol is B♭7. The dominant seventh chord is the same as the major seventh chord except the seventh is lowered one half step, just like it is in the Mixolydian scale. If you can play B♭MA7, all you have to do is lower the seventh to play B♭7.

Accompaniment Grooves

Use this Accompaniment Groove for exercise **A** and **Improvisation Practice**.

Use this Accompaniment Groove for exercise **B** and **D**.

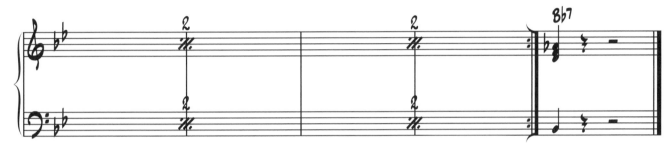

Improvisation Practice

Improvisation Practice takes you through the solo section of *Quarterback Sneak* two times. Even though the chords change, you can improvise over the entire solo section using pitches from the B♭ Mixolydian scale.

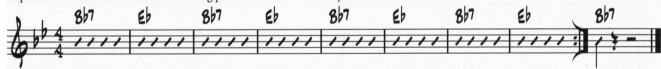

☑ Let's Check Progress

			Practiced		Mastered
Piano Spotlight	**A**				
	B				
	C				
Rhythm Sectional	**4**				

B♭ Mixolydian

			Practiced		Mastered
A	Play				
B1	As Written				
	Improv Practice				
B2	As Written				
	Improv Practice				
B3	As Written				
	Improv Practice				
B4	As Written				
	Improv Practice				
C	Write				
	Play				

Apply what you have learned from the Jazz Starters as you play the *Quarterback Sneak* **Jazz Ensemble Chart** on pages 8 and 9 or **Lead Sheet** on page 51B.

Concert B♭

Quarterback Sneak

Piano

Dean Sorenson

*To practice soloing on this chart, use the solo section accompaniment groove recording in your *Interactive Practice Studio*. The written solo is played the first time through.

A Darker Shade of Gray
Piano Spotlight

 Use the recordings and other features included in the *First Place for Jazz Interactive Practice Studio*. See page 1 for more details.

Exercise A will help you practice the basic rhythm section groove for the solo section of *A Darker Shade of Gray*. The bass clef doubles the bass line, and is included in case your director asks you to play it. On the recording, you will hear the treble clef part only.

Whenever you see chord symbols in a part, you are free to create your own part instead of playing the written groove. If you choose to create your own part, make certain it is consistent with the style and harmony of the music.

Concert B♭

A

When playing tunes in a swing style, like *A Darker Shade of Gray*, piano players typically create their own part based on the chord changes. This is called comping. The written piano part in the treble clef above is an example of a comped part that approaches the chord tones by step. You can begin to learn about comping by studying the following exercises.

Comping is the combination of chord voicings and improvised rhythms. Exercise B1 demonstrates a possible chord voicing, followed by a sample comping rhythm. They come together at the end of the exercise. Exercise B1 is not recorded.

B1

JAZZ THEORY The chord **voicing** is the vertical arrangement of the different notes of the chord. The **comping rhythm** is the rhythm that the chord voicings are played in.

Exercise B2 is an example of a piano part that does not include written voicings. Parts like this include chord symbols and slashes. It is up to the player to create the voicings and the comping rhythms. Even though piano parts are often written like Exercise B2, all of the piano parts in *First Place for Jazz* are written out. Exercise B2 is not recorded.

B2

Exercise B3 is an example of what a piano player could actually play when using the voicing and rhythm from Exercise B1. Listen carefully to the recording and match it as closely as possible.

B3

Exercise C contains variations of the comping rhythm in Exercise B1. Feel free to experiment with your own comping rhythms. Exercise C is not recorded.

C

JAZZ THEORY **Comping rhythms** are usually fairly simple and repetitive. Take care not to make them too complicated.

☐ Check your progress on page 11 after each exercise. ➤

LESSON 1 - Begin with Bass and Hi-hat

Listen as the bass and hi-hat play. Focus on rhythm, tempo, and balance. Your director may ask you to play the bass clef part of your music from Lesson 2 if there is no bass player in the ensemble, or to reinforce the bass line. The bass clef of the piano part is identical to the bass part.

 A Darker Shade of Gray is in a **swing** style. When playing swing tunes the eighth notes should be phrased as triplets (♫ = ♩♪). The overall feel should be relaxed but still moving forward.

LESSON 2 - Add Piano and Vibes

Play the exercise, focusing on rhythm, tempo, and balance. Listen carefully to the recording and match it as closely as possible.

Note: This exercise is not repeated on the recording.

 Guitar, piano, and vibes are **comping** instruments. Comping is a technique used to ac**comp**any or **comp**lement the parts played by the other members of the ensemble. It involves creating a rhythmically-appropriate part that follows the chord changes of the music.

LESSON 3 - Add Guitar, Ride Cymbal, and Congas

Play your part from Lesson 2, focusing on rhythm, tempo, and balance. Match the recording as closely as possible.

 The **ride pattern** played by the drummer on the ride cymbal is a critical part of a swing groove. Listen to it carefully on the recordings and any time you listen to swing music.

LESSON 4 - Add Kick Drum - Complete Groove

Play your part from Lesson 2, focusing on rhythm, tempo, and balance. Match the recording as closely as possible.

 A cymbal crash is often played by the drummer at the beginning of each section of the piece, or when a section repeats. This is important to help **mark the form**, for performers and listeners.

Practice your part by using the **rhythm section practice track** for your instrument.

Concert B♭

Concert Bb

Bb Dorian Scale

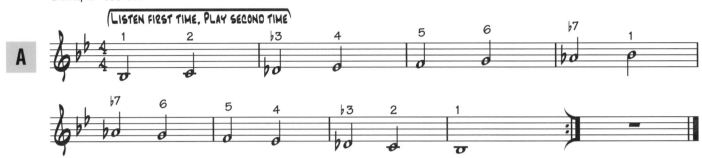

JAZZ THEORY *A Darker Shade of Gray* uses the **Bb Dorian scale**. The Dorian scale is the same as the major scale except the third and seventh degrees are lowered one half step. This is why the third and seventh degrees of the Dorian scale are labeled as b**3** and b**7**. If you can play the Bb major scale, all you have to do is lower the third and seventh to play the Bb Dorian scale.

Bb Dorian Pitch Sets

After listening to and playing each Pitch Set as written, skip to **Improvisation Practice** and play a solo using only those scale degrees.

Start with 1 and b7

Add 2 and 6

Add b3 and 5

Use any scale degree. Write the scale degrees above the notes before you play.

Bb Minor Seventh Chord — Bbmi7

Lower 3 and 7 one half step.

Write a Bbmi7 chord in the staff below.

Write half note chord tones for Bbmi7 as indicated in the staff below. There is no key signature, so don't forget to add accidentals. Play the chord tones to hear the relationships.

JAZZ THEORY In *A Darker Shade of Gray*, the **minor seventh chord** built on Bb is used. The chord symbol is Bbmi7. The minor seventh chord is the same as the major seventh chord except the third and seventh are lowered one half step, just like they are in the Dorian scale. If you can play Bbma7, all you have to do is lower the third and seventh to play Bbmi7.

Accompaniment Grooves

Use this Accompaniment Groove for exercise **A** and **Improvisation Practice** .

Use this Accompaniment Groove for exercise **B** and **D** .

Improvisation Practice

Improvisation Practice takes you through the solo section of *A Darker Shade of Gray* two times. You can improvise over the entire solo section using pitches from the B♭ Dorian scale.

☑ Let's Check Progress

		Practiced			Mastered
	A				
	B1				
Piano Spotlight	**B2**				
	B3				
	C				
Rhythm Sectional	**4**				

B♭ Dorian

		Practiced			Mastered
A	Play				
B1	As Written				
	Improv Practice				
B2	As Written				
	Improv Practice				
B3	As Written				
	Improv Practice				
B4	As Written				
	Improv Practice				
C	Write				
	Play				

Apply what you have learned from the Jazz Starters as you play the *A Darker Shade of Gray* **Jazz Ensemble Chart** on pages 12 and 13 or **Lead Sheet** on page 52.

Concert B♭

A Darker Shade of Gray

Dean Sorenson

*To practice soloing on this chart, use the solo section accompaniment groove recording in your *Interactive Practice Studio*. The written solo is played the first time through.

Pink Flamingo Night
Piano Spotlight

Use the recordings and other features included in the *First Place for Jazz Interactive Practice Studio*. See page 1 for more details.

Exercise A will help you practice the basic rhythm section groove for the solo section of *Pink Flamingo Night*. The bass clef doubles the bass line, and is included in case your director asks you to play it. On the recording, you will hear the treble clef part only.

Concert Bb

A

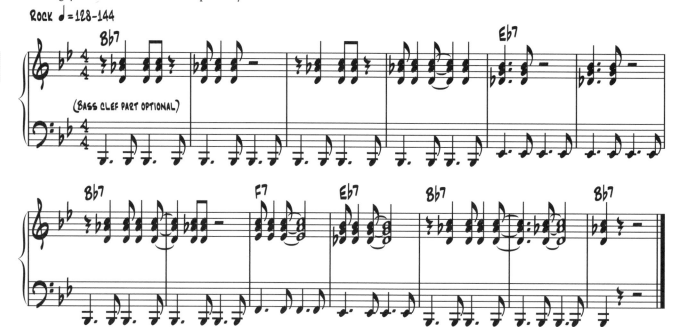

Pink Flamingo Night is a blues chord progression and piano players often create their own comped part when playing blues progressions. Since the blues progression contains three different chords, the comping exercises in B1 through B3 will focus on applying different comping rhythms to the given voicings. Exercises B1 through B3 are not recorded.

B1

B2

B3

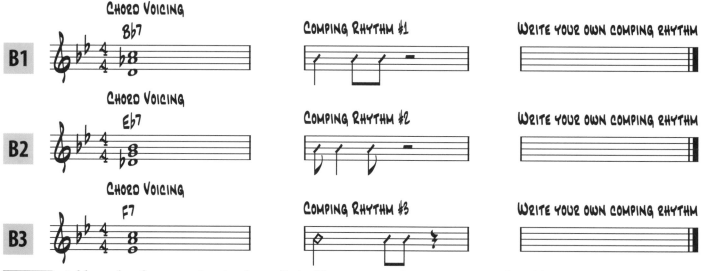

JAZZ THEORY A **blues chord progression** is often called a **blues progression**, or more simply, a **blues**. A **chord progression** is the movement of the different chords of a tune. Most blues progressions are 12 bars long. There are countless variations of the blues progression, but the most basic blues uses chords built on the root, 4th, and 5th degrees of the tonic scale.

Exercise C is a practice track that will help you to create you own comping rhythms. Use the chord voicings from Exercise B1, B2, and B3. Feel free to experiment with various comping rhythms within the context of the music.

C

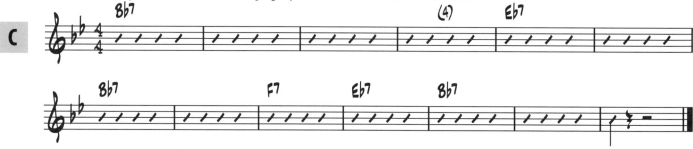

JAZZ THEORY Exercise C is an example of how more advanced piano parts are often written. The **slash markings** mean that you should create your own comping rhythms and voicings using the given chord symbols. This exercise is only for reference, as all of the piano parts in *First Place for Jazz* are written out.

☐ Check your progress on page 15 after each exercise. ▶

LESSON 1 - Begin with Bass, Kick Drum, and Snare Drum

Listen as the bass, kick drum, and snare drum play. Focus on rhythm, tempo, and balance. Your director may ask you to play the bass clef part of your music from Lesson 3 if there is no bass player in the ensemble, or to reinforce the bass line. The bass clef of the piano part is identical to the bass part.

 The series of chords that makes up a song is called the **chord progression**. The basic **blues progression** or simply **blues** is a series of three chords played over 12 bars. The **12 bar blues** is the most common musical form in jazz.

LESSON 2 - Add Guitar

Listen as the bass, kick drum, snare drum, and guitar play. Focus on rhythm, tempo, and balance. Your director may ask you to play the bass clef part of your music from Lesson 3 if there is no bass player in the ensemble, or to reinforce the bass line.

LESSON 3 - Add Piano, Vibes, Cowbell, and Tambourine

Play the exercise, focusing on rhythm, tempo, and balance. Play only the treble clef part unless your director asks you to play the bass part. Listen carefully to the recording and match it as closely as possible.

Note: This exercise is not repeated on the recording.

 Backbeats (beats 2 and 4 in $\frac{4}{4}$) are fundamental to the rhythmic drive of the rock groove. They are usually played on snare drum in rock styles.

LESSON 4 - Add Hi-hat and Crash Cymbal - Complete Groove

Play your part from Lesson 3, focusing on rhythm, tempo, and balance. Match the recording as closely as possible.

 A cymbal crash is often played by the drummer at the beginning of each section of the piece, or when a section repeats. This is important to help **mark the form**, for performers and listeners.

Practice your part by using the **rhythm section practice track** for your instrument.

Concert B♭

B♭ Blues Scale

A

Rock ♩ = 128–144

LISTEN FIRST TIME, PLAY SECOND TIME

> **JAZZ THEORY** *Pink Flamingo Night* uses the **B♭ blues scale**. The blues scale differs from the major scale in several significant ways: 1) the third and seventh degrees are lowered one half step; 2) the second and sixth degrees are omitted; 3) a fifth degree lowered one half step is added (notated as ♯4 for ease of reading).

B♭ Blues Pitch Sets

After listening to and playing each Pitch Set as written, skip to **Improvisation Practice** and play a solo using only those scale degrees.

B1 — Start with 1 and ♭7 — LISTEN / PLAY

B2 — Add ♭3 and 4

B3 — Add ♯4(♭5) and 5

Use any scale degree. Write the scale degrees above the notes before you play.

B4

B♭ Blues Dominant Seventh Chords — B♭⁷, E♭⁷, F⁷

Write half note chord tones for **B♭⁷**, **E♭⁷**, and **F⁷** as indicated in the staff below.
There is no key signature, so don't forget to add accidentals.
Play the chord tones to hear the relationships.

C

> **JAZZ THEORY** *Pink Flamingo Night* uses a **blues progression**. A **progression** is a series of chords. The basic **B♭ blues progression** is comprised of three dominant seventh chords built on B♭, E♭, and F. The chord symbols are **B♭⁷**, **E♭⁷**, and **F⁷**.

Accompaniment Grooves

Use this Accompaniment Groove for exercise **A** and **Improvisation Practice** .

Use this Accompaniment Groove for exercise **B** and **D** .

Improvisation Practice

Improvisation Practice takes you through the solo section of *Pink Flamingo Night* two times. Even though the chords change, you can improvise over the entire solo section using pitches from the B♭ blues scale.

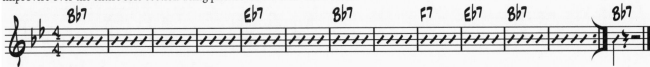

☑ Let's Check Progress

		Practiced		Mastered
Piano Spotlight	**A**			
	B1			
	B2			
	B3			
	C			
Rhythm Sectional	**4**			

B♭ Blues

		Practiced		Mastered
A	Play			
B1	As Written			
	Improv Practice			
B2	As Written			
	Improv Practice			
B3	As Written			
	Improv Practice			
B4	As Written			
	Improv Practice			
C	Write			
	Play			

Apply what you have learned from the Jazz Starters as you play the *Pink Flamingo Night*
Jazz Ensemble Chart on pages 16 and 17 or **Lead Sheet** on page 52B.

Pink Flamingo Night

Piano

Dean Sorenson

*To practice soloing on this chart, use the solo section accompaniment groove recording in your *Interactive Practice Studio*. The written solo is played the first time through.

Summer in São Paulo
Piano Spotlight

Use the recordings and other features included in the *First Place for Jazz Interactive Practice Studio*. See page 1 for more details.

Exercise A will help you practice the basic rhythm section groove of *Summer in São Paulo*. Unlike the piano parts from earlier in the book, the chord voicings for *Summer in São Paulo* are written in both treble and bass clef. You should play with both hands all the time. Listen carefully to the recording and match it as closely as possible.

A

The *Summer in São Paulo* jazz ensemble chart includes several passages that are marked "As Is." Passages marked "As Is" do not include chord symbols because you are expected to play exactly what is written. Exercise B is taken from the *Summer in São Paulo* jazz ensemble chart and includes a series of band figures. Practice this exercise until you can play it comfortably.

B

Concert F

JAZZ THEORY   A **band figure** is a rhythm that is played by the entire ensemble. Playing figures is different than playing accompaniment grooves, because your part has to match the rest of the ensemble exactly.

Exercise C is another "As Is" passage from the *Summer in São Paulo* jazz ensemble chart. Match the recording as closely as possible.

C

JAZZ THEORY   The markings above the notes are **articulations**. These markings tell you to play a note long or short, with emphasis (accented), or without. The recording demonstrates these articulations.

Check your progress on page 19 after each exercise. ➡

LESSON 1 - Establish Figures with No Drum Fills

Play the exercise, focusing on rhythm, tempo, and balance. Listen carefully to the recording and match it as closely as possible.

Note: This exercise is not repeated on the recording.

 Figures are portions of the rhythm section parts that often duplicate rhythms in the ensemble parts. Figures help to reinforce these ensemble rhythms.

LESSON 2 - Add Kick Drum and Ending Fill Only

Play your part from Lesson 1, focusing on rhythm, tempo, and balance. Match the recording as closely as possible.

 Marking the form means that the transitions between major phrases in the music are clearly outlined.

LESSON 3 - Add Drum Fills as Written

Play your part from Lesson 1, focusing on rhythm, tempo, and balance. Match the recording as closely as possible.

LESSON 4 - Add Improvised Drum Fills

Play your part from Lesson 1, focusing on rhythm, tempo, and balance. Match the recording as closely as possible.

Practice your part by using the **rhythm section practice track** for your instrument.

Concert F

F Major Scale

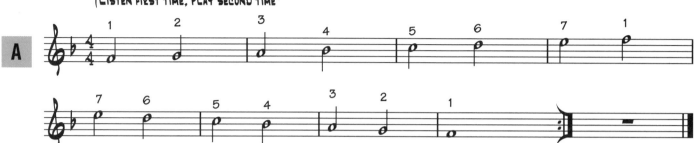

JAZZ THEORY *Summer in São Paulo* uses the **F major scale**. It is the same as the scale used for *Jumpin' Jellybeans* (pp. 2-5), only now it is built on F instead of B♭. F is now the first degree or tonic.

F Major Pitch Sets

After listening to and playing each Pitch Set as written, skip to **Improvisation Practice** and play a solo using only those scale degrees.

Concert F

Use any scale degree. Write the scale degrees above the notes before you play.

F Major Seventh Chord — FMA7

Write an FMA7 chord in the staff below.

Write half note chord tones for FMA7 as indicated in the staff below. There is no key signature, so don't forget to add accidentals. Play the chord tones to hear the relationships.

JAZZ THEORY In *Summer in São Paulo*, the major seventh chord built on F is used. The chord symbol is FMA7. Remember, the chord tones correspond to the first, third, fifth, and seventh degrees of the major scale.

Accompaniment Grooves

Use this Accompaniment Groove for exercise **A** and **Improvisation Practice** .

1

Use this Accompaniment Groove for exercise **B** and **D** .

2

Concert F

Improvisation Practice

Improvisation Practice takes you through the solo section of *Summer in São Paulo* two times. Even though the chords change, you can improvise over the entire solo section using pitches from the F major scale.

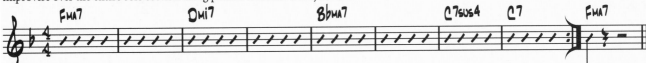

✓ Let's Check Progress

F Major

			Practiced			Mastered
A	Play					
B1	As Written					
	Improv Practice					
B2	As Written					
	Improv Practice					
B3	As Written					
	Improv Practice					
B4	As Written					
	Improv Practice					
C	Write					
	Play					

			Practiced			Mastered
Piano Spotlight	**A**					
	B					
	C					
Rhythm Sectional	**4**					

Apply what you have learned from the Jazz Starters as you play the *Summer in São Paulo* **Jazz Ensemble Chart** on pages 20 and 21 or **Lead Sheet** on page 53.

Summer in São Paulo

Piano

Dean Sorenson

*To practice soloing on this chart, use the solo section accompaniment groove recording in your *Interactive Practice Studio*. The written solo is played the first time through.

The Lady Knows Her Cheese
Piano Spotlight

Use the recordings and other features included in the *First Place for Jazz Interactive Practice Studio*. See page 1 for more details.

Piano players often have to play written lines in addition to comping. These written lines usually double other parts in the ensemble. Exercise A will help you practice one of the written lines from *The Lady Knows Her Cheese* jazz ensemble chart. Listen carefully to the recording and match it as closely as possible.

JAZZ THEORY The markings above the notes are called **articulations** and are commonly included in ensemble parts. They are included here since your line doubles the horn line. Articulations provide detailed information on exactly how long, short, or accented a note should be played. The following explains the different articulation markings.

> Play the note accented and long.   ∧ Play the note accented and short.   — Play the note long.   • Play the note short.

Exercise B will help you practice the basic rhythm section groove for the solo section of *The Lady Knows Her Cheese*. When playing a basic groove like this, you are comping. Make certain to play with a firm touch on the keys, and avoid the sustain pedal.

JAZZ THEORY **Comping** is the combination of chord voicings and improvised rhythms.

Exercise C is another "As Is" passage from *The Lady Knows Her Cheese* jazz ensemble chart. Match the recording as closely as possible.

☐ Check your progress on page 23 after each exercise. ➤

LESSON 1 - Establish Solid Tempo with No Figures or Fills

Play the exercise, focusing on rhythm, tempo, and balance. Listen carefully to the recording and match it as closely as possible.

 Figures are portions of the rhythm section parts that often duplicate rhythms in the ensemble parts. Figures help to reinforce these ensemble rhythms.

LESSON 2 - Add Figures in Drums with Hands Only

Play your part from Lesson 1, focusing on rhythm, tempo, and balance. Match the recording as closely as possible.

 Marking the form means that the transitions between major phrases in the music are clearly outlined.

LESSON 3 - Add Hi-hat to Figures

Play your part from Lesson 1, focusing on rhythm, tempo, and balance. Match the recording as closely as possible.

LESSON 4 - Add Kick Drum and Fills

Play your part from Lesson 1, focusing on rhythm, tempo, and balance. Match the recording as closely as possible.

Practice your part by using the **rhythm section practice track** for your instrument.

Concert F

Concert F

F Mixolydian Scale

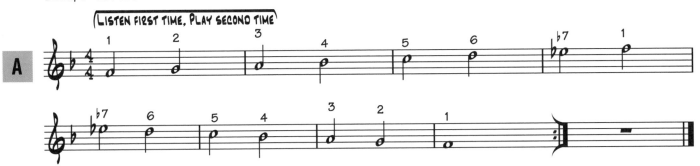

A

JAZZ THEORY *The Lady Knows Her Cheese* uses the **F Mixolydian scale**. It is the same as the scale used for *Quarterback Sneak* (pp. 6-9), only now it is built on F instead of B♭. Remember, the Mixolydian scale matches the major scale except the seventh degree is lowered one half step. If you can play the F major scale, all you have to do is lower the seventh to play the F Mixolydian scale.

F Mixolydian Pitch Sets

After listening to and playing each Pitch Set as written, skip to **Improvisation Practice** and play a solo using only those scale degrees.

Start with 1 and ♭7

B1

Add 2 and 6

B2

Add 3 and 5

B3

Use any scale degree. Write the scale degrees above the notes before you play.

B4

F Dominant Seventh Chord — F⁷

Lower 7 one half step.

Write an F⁷ chord in the staff below.

Write half note chord tones for F⁷ as indicated in the staff below. There is no key signature, so don't forget to add accidentals. Play the chord tones to hear the relationships.

C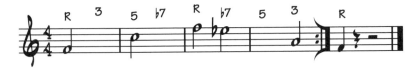

JAZZ THEORY In *The Lady Knows Her Cheese*, the dominant seventh chord built on F is used. The chord symbol is F⁷. It is the same as the chord learned in *Quarterback Sneak* (pp. 6-9), only now it is built on F instead of B♭. Remember, the dominant seventh chord matches the major seventh chord except the seventh is lowered one half step, just like it is in the Mixolydian scale. If you can play FMA7, all you have to do is lower the seventh to play F⁷.

Accompaniment Grooves

Use this Accompaniment Groove for exercise A and **Improvisation Practice**.

SWING ♩ = 124-138

Use this Accompaniment Groove for exercise B and D.

Concert F

Improvisation Practice

Improvisation Practice takes you through the solo section of *The Lady Knows Her Cheese* two times. You can improvise over the entire solo section using pitches from the F Mixolydian scale.

☑ Let's Check Progress

F Mixolydian

				Practiced		Mastered
A	Play					
B1	As Written					
	Improv Practice					
B2	As Written					
	Improv Practice					
B3	As Written					
	Improv Practice					
B4	As Written					
	Improv Practice					
C	Write					
	Play					

			Practiced		Mastered
Piano Spotlight	**A**				
	B				
	C				
Rhythm Sectional	**4**				

Apply what you have learned from the Jazz Starters as you play *The Lady Knows Her Cheese* **Jazz Ensemble Chart** on pages 24 and 25 or **Lead Sheet** on page 53B. ➡

The Lady Knows Her Cheese

Dean Sorenson

Piano

Concert F

*To practice soloing on this chart, use the solo section accompaniment groove recording in your *Interactive Practice Studio*. The written solo is played the first time through.

Lucky Seven
Piano Spotlight

Use the recordings and other features included in the *First Place for Jazz Interactive Practice Studio*. See page 1 for more details.

The groove for *Lucky Seven* has two different feels. Exercises A and B will help you practice your part for each. The groove that is used for the majority of the chart is presented in Exercise A. Be sure to follow the articulation markings carefully. The bass clef of the piano part doubles the bass line, and is included in case your director asks you to play it. On the recording, you will hear the treble clef part only. Listen carefully to the recording and match it as closely as possible.

Exercise B is the contrasting feel. This is called a half time feel, and you will get a much clearer idea of what it should sound like by listening to the full recording of the *Lucky Seven* jazz ensemble chart.

JAZZ THEORY **Half time feel** gives the illusion of the tempo slowing down by half but in reality the bars keep moving along at the same speed.

Exercise C is a passage from the *Lucky Seven* jazz ensemble chart that will help you to practice transitioning between the two different feels. Note how the bass clef of the piano part is added when the music is marked "As Is." Match the recording as closely as possible.

JAZZ THEORY Piano parts often use shorthand to notate repetitive music. The marking used in bars 3 through 4 means you should play the same music from the previous two bars.

☐ Check your progress on page 27 after each exercise. ➤➤➤

LESSON 1 - Establish Main Groove

Play the exercise, focusing on rhythm, tempo, and balance. Follow the marked articulations. Listen carefully to the recording and match it as closely as possible.

Note: This exercise is not repeated on the recording.

J A Z Z PERFORMANCE A **4-feel** means a strong pulse on all four beats of the measure, while a **2-feel**, means the pulse is felt stronger on beats one and three. The 2-feel is often called **half time feel**. Listen carefully to the recording to aurally distinguish between 4-feel and 2-feel.

LESSON 2 - Establish Contrasting Feel

Play the exercise, listening carefully to how your part fits in with the rest of the rhythm section. Match the recording as closely as possible.

Note: This exercise is not repeated on the recording.

J A Z Z PERFORMANCE **Half time feel** gives the illusion of the tempo slowing down by half but in reality the bars keep moving along at the same speed.

LESSON 3 - Transition Between the Two Different Feels

Play the exercise, focusing on rhythm, tempo, and balance. Match the recording as closely as possible.

LESSON 4 - Transition with Ending Figure

Play the exercise, focusing on rhythm, tempo, and balance. Match the recording as closely as possible.

Practice your part by using the **rhythm section practice track** for your instrument.

Concert F

W75P

F Dorian Scale

 Lucky Seven uses the **F Dorian scale**. It is the same as the scale used for *A Darker Shade of Gray* (pp. 10-13), only now it is built on F instead of B♭. Remember, the Dorian scale matches the major scale except the third and seventh degrees are lowered one half step. If you can play the F major scale, all you have to do is lower the third and seventh to play the F Dorian scale.

F Dorian Pitch Sets

After listening to and playing each Pitch Set as written, skip to **Improvisation Practice** and play a solo using only those scale degrees.

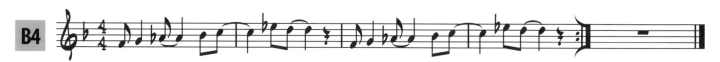

Use any scale degree. Write the scale degrees above the notes before you play.

F Minor Seventh Chord — FMI7

 In *Lucky Seven*, the minor seventh chord built on F is used. The chord symbol is FMI7. It is the same as the chord learned in *A Darker Shade of Gray* (pp. 10-13), only now it is built on F instead of B♭. Remember, the minor seventh chord matches the major seventh chord except the third and seventh are lowered one half step, just like they are in the Dorian scale. If you can play FMA7, all you have to do is lower the third and seventh to play FMI7.

Accompaniment Grooves

Use this Accompaniment Groove for exercise **A** and **Improvisation Practice**.

Use this Accompaniment Groove for exercise **B** and **D**.

Improvisation Practice

Improvisation Practice takes you through the solo section of *Lucky Seven* two times. Even though the chords change, you can improvise over the entire solo section using pitches from the F Dorian scale.

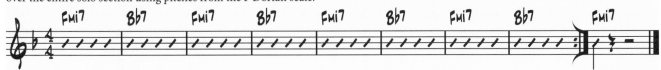

✓ Let's Check Progress

			Practiced			Mastered
Piano Spotlight	**A**					
	B					
	C					
Rhythm Sectional	**4**					

F Dorian

			Practiced			Mastered
A	Play					
B1	As Written					
	Improv Practice					
B2	As Written					
	Improv Practice					
B3	As Written					
	Improv Practice					
B4	As Written					
	Improv Practice					
C	Write					
	Play					

Apply what you have learned from the Jazz Starters as you play the *Lucky Seven* **Jazz Ensemble Chart** on pages 28 and 29 or **Lead Sheet** on page 54.

Lucky Seven

Piano

Dean Sorenson

*To practice soloing on this chart, use the solo section accompaniment groove recording in your *Interactive Practice Studio*. The written solo is played the first time through.

Use the recordings and other features included in the *First Place for Jazz Interactive Practice Studio*. See page 1 for more details.

The piano groove for *Chasing the Sun* is a montuno. The following exercises will give you the opportunity to practice the different arpeggios of this montuno. Each example is recorded at a slower practice tempo, and also at the performance tempo. Montuno parts are very busy and complex. There are few opportunities to rest and the rhythmic drive must remain constant throughout. By breaking up the montuno into smaller elements and slowing it down you will be able to internalize it much better.

Exercises A1 through A3 isolate the three different arpeggios that make up the entire chord progression. Get comfortable with these exercises at the slower tempo, then move up to the performance tempo. Listen carefully to all of the recordings and match them as closely as possible. Use both hands to play the part as written in the treble clef. The bass clef is omitted from these exercises as it is rarely played by the piano player in this style of music.

JAZZ THEORY A **montuno** is a syncopated and often arpeggiated pattern played by the piano in Latin music.

Switching the montuno pattern from one chord to the next is often the most challenging part of playing this kind of groove. Exercises B1 through B4 will help you practice the different chord transitions. On the recording, these exercises are played at a slower tempo and then at performance tempo. Listen carefully to all of the recordings and match them as closely as possible.

Concert F

Exercise C is a passage taken from the *Chasing the Sun* jazz ensemble chart that will help you put all of the above exercises together to play the entire groove. Match the recording as closely as possible.

JAZZ PERFORMANCE **Salsa** is a type of Latin jazz that combines the folk music of Cuba, Puerto Rico, and the Spanish Caribbean with elements of rhythm-and-blues, pop, and jazz.

☐ Check your progress on page 31 after each exercise. ━━━▶

LESSON 1 - Establish the Clave Rhythm

Clap this exercise, focusing on rhythm and tempo. This exercise will help you internalize the clave rhythm. Listen carefully to the recording and match it as closely as possible.

 JAZZ PERFORMANCE The **clave** is the primary rhythm in salsa, as it is in most Latin styles. Different styles of Latin music may have different clave rhythms. Clave in this context refers to a rhythm pattern and not the percussion instrument called claves.

LESSON 2 - Add Bass and Kick Drum

Clap your part from Lesson 1, focusing on rhythm, tempo, and balance. Match the recording as closely as possible.

JAZZ PERFORMANCE Listen carefully to the bass part and note when the bass line lands on beat 4 and is tied across the barline. It is important that everyone in the band is aware of this unique rhythm found in salsa style bass lines.

LESSON 3 - Add Guitar, Piano, Vibes, and Congas

Play the exercise, focusing on rhythm, tempo, and balance. Match the recording as closely as possible.

JAZZ PERFORMANCE A **montuno** is a syncopated and often arpeggiated pattern played by the piano in Latin music.

LESSON 4 - Add Ride Cymbal - Complete Groove

Play your part from Lesson 3, focusing on rhythm, tempo, and balance. Match the recording as closely as possible.

Practice your part by using the **rhythm section practice track** for your instrument.

Concert F

Concert F

F Blues Scale

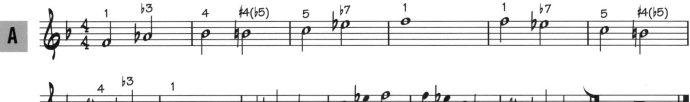

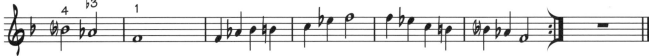

JAZZ THEORY *Chasing the Sun* uses the **F blues scale**. It is the same as the scale used for *Pink Flamingo Night* (pp. 14-17), only now it is built on F instead of B♭. Remember, the blues scale differs from the major scale in several significant ways: 1) the third and seventh degrees are lowered one half step; 2) the second and sixth degrees are omitted; 3) a fifth degree lowered one half step is added (notated as #4 for ease of reading).

F Blues Pitch Sets

After listening to and playing each Pitch Set as written, skip to **Improvisation Practice** and play a solo using only those scale degrees.

B1 Start with 1 and ♭7

B2 Add ♭3 and 4

B3 Add #4(♭5) and 5

Use any scale degree. Write the scale degrees above the notes before you play.

B4

F Blues Dominant Seventh Chords — F7, B♭7, C7

Write half note chord tones for **F7**, **B♭7**, and **C7** as indicated in the staff below.
There is no key signature, so don't forget to add accidentals.
Play the chord tones to hear the relationships.

C

JAZZ THEORY Like *Pink Flamingo Night* (pp. 14-17), *Chasing the Sun* uses a blues progression comprised of three dominant seventh chords. This time the chords are built on F, B♭, and C to create an **F blues progression**. The chord symbols are **F7**, **B♭7**, and **C7**.

Accompaniment Grooves

Use this Accompaniment Groove for exercise **A** and **Improvisation Practice** .

SALSA ♩=160-172

1

Use this Accompaniment Groove for exercise **B** and **D** .

2

Concert F

Improvisation Practice

Improvisation Practice takes you through the solo section of *Chasing the Sun* two times. Even though the chords change, you can improvise over the entire solo section using pitches from the F blues scale.

✓ Let's Check Progress

			Practiced		Mastered
Piano Spotlight	**A** 1-3				
	B 1-4				
	C				
Rhythm Sectional	**4**				

F Blues

			Practiced		Mastered
A	Play				
B1	As Written				
	Improv Practice				
B2	As Written				
	Improv Practice				
B3	As Written				
	Improv Practice				
B4	As Written				
	Improv Practice				
C	Write				
	Play				

Apply what you have learned from the Jazz Starters as you play the *Chasing the Sun* **Jazz Ensemble Chart** on pages 32 and 33 or **Lead Sheet** on page 54B .

Chasing the Sun

Piano

Dean Sorenson

*To practice soloing on this chart, use the solo section accompaniment groove recording in your *Interactive Practice Studio*. The written solo is played the first time through.

Use the recordings and other features included in the *First Place for Jazz Interactive Practice Studio*. See page 1 for more details.

Exercise A will help you practice the basic rhythm section groove for the solo section of *Evening Stroll*. It is common in swing styles for chord voicings to be written in both treble and bass clef. You should play with both hands all the time. Listen carefully to the recording and match it as closely as possible.

A

The *Evening Stroll* jazz ensemble chart includes two passages that are marked "As Is." Passages marked "As Is" do not include chord symbols because you are expected to play exactly what is written. Exercise B will help you practice the first "As Is" passage which includes a series of band figures. Match the recording as closely as possible.

B

JAZZ THEORY A **band figure** is a rhythm that is played by the entire ensemble. Playing figures is different than playing accompaniment grooves, because your part has to match the rest of the ensemble exactly.

Exercise C will help you practice the second "As Is" passage from the *Evening Stroll* jazz ensemble chart. Match the recording as closely as possible.

C

JAZZ THEORY The markings above the notes are **articulations**. These markings tell you to play a note long or short, with emphasis (accented), or without. The recording demonstrates these articulations.

Concert E♭

☐ Check your progress on page 35 after each exercise.

LESSON 1 - Begin with Bass and Hi-hat

Listen as the bass and hi-hat play. Focus on rhythm, tempo, and balance.

 The **root** is the fundamental note of the chord. The root of the chord is the note named in the chord symbol (in an E♭ma7 chord, "E♭" is the root).

LESSON 2 - Add Piano, Vibes, and Ride Cymbal

Play the exercise, focusing on rhythm, tempo, and balance. Listen carefully to the recording and match it as closely as possible.

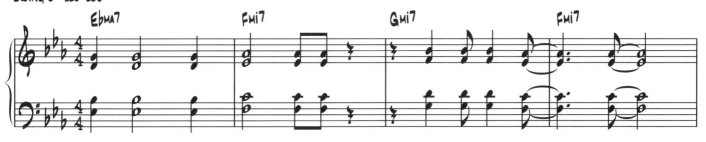

Note: This exercise is not repeated on the recording.

 The guitar, piano, and vibes are **comping** instruments. Comping is a technique used to ac**comp**any or **comp**lement the parts played by the other members of the ensemble. It involves creating a rhythmically-appropriate part that follows the chord changes of the music.

LESSON 3 - Add Guitar and Congas

Play your part from Lesson 2, focusing on rhythm, tempo, and balance. Match the recording as closely as possible.

 When the guitar plays repeated downstrokes in a swing tune it is often called **Freddie Green Style**, named for the famous guitarist who played with the Count Basie Orchestra for over 50 years.

LESSON 4 - Add Kick Drum - Complete Groove

Play your part from Lesson 2, trading off comping duties with guitar and vibes.

Practice your part by using the **rhythm section practice track** for your instrument.

Concert E♭

E♭ Major Scale

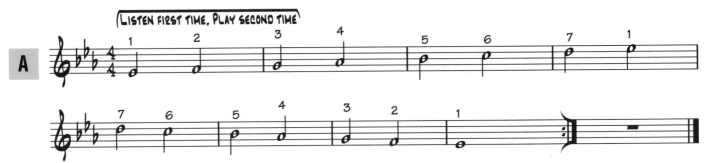

JAZZ THEORY *Evening Stroll* uses the **E♭ major scale**. It is the same as the scale used for *Jumpin' Jellybeans* (pp. 2-5) and *Summer in São Paulo* (pp. 18-21), only now it is built on E♭. E♭ is now the first degree or tonic.

E♭ Major Pitch Sets

After listening to and playing each Pitch Set as written, skip to **Improvisation Practice** and play a solo using only those scale degrees.

Start with 1 and 7

B1

Add 2 and 6

B2

Add 3 and 5

B3

Use any scale degree. Write the scale degrees above the notes before you play.

B4

E♭ Major Seventh Chord — E♭MA7

Write an E♭MA7 chord in the staff below.

Write half note chord tones for E♭MA7 as indicated in the staff below. There is no key signature, so don't forget to add accidentals. Play the chord tones to hear the relationships.

C

JAZZ THEORY In *Evening Stroll*, the major seventh chord built on E♭ is used. The chord symbol is E♭MA7. Remember, the chord tones correspond to the first, third, fifth, and seventh degrees of the major scale.

Accompaniment Grooves

Use this Accompaniment Groove for exercise **A** and **Improvisation Practice**.

1

Use this Accompaniment Groove for exercise **B** and **D**.

2

Improvisation Practice

Improvisation Practice takes you through the solo section of *Evening Stroll* two times. Even though the chords change, you can improvise over the entire solo section using pitches from the E♭ major scale.

✓ Let's Check Progress

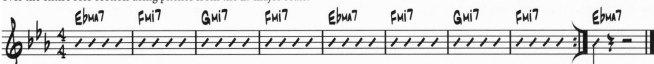

		Practiced			Mastered
Piano Spotlight	**A**				
	B				
	C				
Rhythm Sectional	**4**				

E♭ Major

			Practiced		Mastered
A	Play				
B1	As Written				
	Improv Practice				
B2	As Written				
	Improv Practice				
B3	As Written				
	Improv Practice				
B4	As Written				
	Improv Practice				
C	Write				
	Play				

Apply what you have learned from the Jazz Starters as you play the *Evening Stroll* **Jazz Ensemble Chart** on pages 36 and 37 or **Lead Sheet** on page 55.

Concert E♭

Evening Stroll

Piano

Dean Sorenson

Concert E♭

*To practice soloing on this chart, use the solo section accompaniment groove recording in your *Interactive Practice Studio*. The written solo is played the first time through.

Use the recordings and other features included in the *First Place for Jazz Interactive Practice Studio*. See page 1 for more details.

Exercise A will help you practice the basic rhythm section groove for the solo section of *Crutch Not Much*. The bass clef part doubles the bass line, and is included in case your director asks you to play it. On the recording, you will hear the treble clef part only.

A

JAZZ THEORY **Chord symbols** are notated on top of the staff and define the chords that are used. The vertical arrangement of the different chord tones is called the chord **voicing**. More advanced jazz piano players create their own voicings from the chord symbols, but in *First Place for Jazz* all of the chord voicings are written out for you.

Exercise B is an ensemble figure that is the introduction to the *Crutch Not Much* jazz ensemble chart. Be sure to bring out the dynamics as marked at the end of the exercise. Listen carefully to the recording and match it as closely as possible.

B

JAZZ THEORY **Dynamics** refer to how loud or soft the music is played.

The *Crutch Not Much* jazz ensemble chart ends with the rhythm section moving smoothly from the groove into a figure very similar to the introduction. Play all notes as marked, including the bass clef. The (-3) at the very end means to release the note on beat 3. Match the recording as closely as possible.

C

JAZZ THEORY The markings above the notes are **articulations**. These markings tell you to play a note long or short, with emphasis (accented), or without. The recording demonstrates these articulations.

☐ Check your progress on page 39 after each exercise.

Concert E♭

LESSON 1 - Opening Band Figure

Play the exercise, focusing on articulations and listening for a "tight" ensemble sound. Play all notes as marked, including the bass clef.

JAZZ PERFORMANCE *Crutch Not Much* is in a **rock** style. Rock styles use straight eighth notes, not swing eighth notes, and should have a very forward-moving rhythmic feel to them.

LESSON 2 - Basic Groove

Play the exercise, focusing on rhythm, tempo, and balance. Omit the bass clef part unless your director asks you to play it. Listen carefully to the recording and match it as closely as possible.

Note: This exercise is not repeated on the recording.

JAZZ PERFORMANCE **Backbeats** (beats 2 and 4 in $\frac{4}{4}$) are fundamental to the rhythmic drive of the rock groove. They are usually played on snare drum in rock styles.

LESSON 3 - Transition Between Figures and Groove

Play the exercise, focusing on rhythm, tempo, and balance. When the groove begins at bar 5, you should omit the bass clef part unless your director asks you to play it. Match the recording as closely as possible.

JAZZ PERFORMANCE Playing rests is just as important as playing notes. The whole rest in bar 4 of this exercise should be "felt" to ensure a solid entrance with the groove in bar 5.

LESSON 4 - Add Short Drum Fill into Groove

Play your part from Lesson 3, focusing on rhythm, tempo, and balance. Match the recording as closely as possible.

Practice your part by using the **rhythm section practice track** for your instrument.

E♭ Mixolydian Scale

JAZZ THEORY *Crutch Not Much* uses the E♭ **Mixolydian scale**. It is the same as the scale used for *Quarterback Sneak* (pp. 6-9) and *The Lady Knows Her Cheese* (pp. 22-25), only now it is built on E♭. Remember, the Mixolydian scale matches the major scale except the seventh degree is lowered one half step. If you can play the E♭ major scale, all you have to do is lower the seventh to play the E♭ Mixolydian scale.

E♭ Mixolydian Pitch Sets

After listening to and playing each Pitch Set as written, skip to **Improvisation Practice** and play a solo using only those scale degrees.

Use any scale degree. Write the scale degrees above the notes before you play.

E♭ Dominant Seventh Chord — E♭⁷

Lower 7 one half step.

Write an E♭⁷ chord in the staff below.

Write half note chord tones for E♭⁷ as indicated in the staff below. There is no key signature, so don't forget to add accidentals. Play the chord tones to hear the relationships.

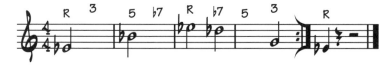

JAZZ THEORY In *Crutch Not Much*, the dominant seventh chord built on E♭ is used. The chord symbol is **E♭⁷**. It is the same as the chord learned in *Quarterback Sneak* (pp. 6-9) and *The Lady Knows Her Cheese* (pp. 22-25), only now it is built on E♭. Remember, the dominant seventh chord matches the major seventh chord except the seventh is lowered one half step, just like it is in the Mixolydian scale. If you can play **E♭ma⁷**, all you have to do is lower the seventh to play **E♭⁷**.

Concert E♭

Accompaniment Grooves

Use this Accompaniment Groove for exercise **A** and **Improvisation Practice**.

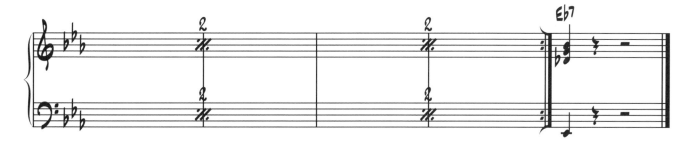

Use this Accompaniment Groove for exercise **B** and **D**.

Improvisation Practice

Improvisation Practice takes you through the solo section of *Crutch Not Much* two times. You can improvise over the entire solo section using pitches from the E♭ Mixolydian scale.

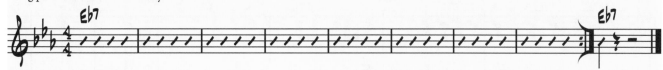

✓ Let's Check Progress

E♭ Mixolydian

Piano Spotlight		Practiced			Mastered
	A				
	B				
	C				
Rhythm Sectional	**4**				

		Practiced			Mastered
A	Play				
B1	As Written				
	Improv Practice				
B2	As Written				
	Improv Practice				
B3	As Written				
	Improv Practice				
B4	As Written				
	Improv Practice				
C	Write				
	Play				

Apply what you have learned from the Jazz Starters as you play the *Crutch Not Much*
Jazz Ensemble Chart on pages 40 and 41 or **Lead Sheet** on page 55B.

Concert E♭

CRUTCH NOT MUCH

PIANO

DEAN SORENSON

Concert E♭

*To practice soloing on this chart, use the solo section accompaniment groove recording in your *Interactive Practice Studio*. The written solo is played the first time through.

Use the recordings and other features included in the *First Place for Jazz Interactive Practice Studio*. See page 1 for more details.

Exercise A will help you practice the basic rhythm section groove for the solo section of *Little Bees*. The bass clef part doubles the bass line, and is included in case your director asks you to play it. On the recording, you will hear the treble clef part only.

JAZZ THEORY The F that is written into the Ebmi7 chord voicing is called an **extension**. Extensions add color to the basic chord tones and are commonly added to chord voicings.

The *Little Bees* jazz ensemble chart includes a contrasting section of music that moves between two different chords and ends with a band figure. Exercise B will help you practice this section of the music. Be sure to make a smooth transition when the chords change. Listen carefully to the recording and match it as closely as possible.

Concert E♭

☐ Check your progress on page 43 after each exercise. ➡

LESSON 1 - Establish Basic Groove

Play the exercise, focusing on rhythm, tempo, and balance. Listen carefully to the recording and match it as closely as possible.

Note: This exercise is not repeated on the recording.

LESSON 2 - Isolate Figure

Play the exercise, focusing on rhythm, tempo, and balance. Match the recording as closely as possible.

LESSON 3 - Transition from Groove to Figure

Play the exercise, moving smoothly from groove to figure. Listen carefully to the drum fill in bar 4 to make a solid entrance on the downbeat in bar 5. Match the recording as closely as possible.

LESSON 4 - Complete Shout Chorus into Figure

Play the exercise, focusing on rhythm, tempo, and balance. Match the recording as closely as possible.

JAZZ PERFORMANCE The **shout chorus** is generally the loudest part of a chart. Play the marked dynamics but always listen for balance.

Concert E♭

Practice your part by using the **rhythm section practice track** for your instrument.

E♭ Dorian Scale

JAZZ THEORY *Little Bees* uses the **E♭ Dorian scale**. It is the same as the scale used for *A Darker Shade of Gray* (pp. 10-13) and *Lucky Seven* (pp. 26-29), only now it is built on E♭. Remember, the Dorian scale matches the major scale except the third and seventh degrees are lowered one half step. If you can play the E♭ major scale, all you have to do is lower the third and seventh to play the E♭ Dorian scale.

E♭ Dorian Pitch Sets

After listening to and playing each Pitch Set as written, skip to **Improvisation Practice** and play a solo using only those scale degrees.

Use any scale degree. Write the scale degrees above the notes before you play.

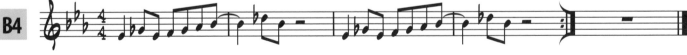

E♭ Minor Seventh Chord — E♭mi7

JAZZ THEORY In *Little Bees*, the minor seventh chord built on E♭ is used. The chord symbol is E♭mi7. It is the same as the chord learned in *A Darker Shade of Gray* (pp. 10-13) and *Lucky Seven* (pp. 26-29), only now it is built on E♭. Remember, the minor seventh chord matches the major seventh chord except the third and seventh are lowered one half step, just like they are in the Dorian scale. If you can play E♭MA7, all you have to do is lower the third and seventh to play E♭mi7.

Accompaniment Grooves

Use this Accompaniment Groove for exercise **A** and **Improvisation Practice** .

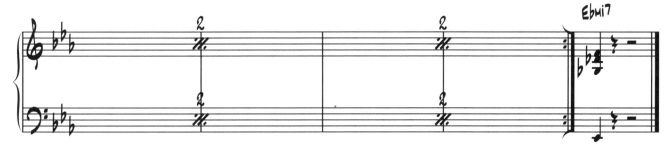

Use this Accompaniment Groove for exercise **B** and **D** .

Improvisation Practice

Improvisation Practice takes you through the solo section of *Little Bees* two times. You can improvise over the entire solo section using pitches from the Eb Dorian scale.

✓ Let's Check Progress

			Practiced			Mastered
Piano Spotlight	**A**					
	B					
Rhythm Sectional	**4**					

Eb Dorian

			Practiced			Mastered
A	Play					
B1	As Written					
	Improv Practice					
B2	As Written					
	Improv Practice					
B3	As Written					
	Improv Practice					
B4	As Written					
	Improv Practice					
C	Write					
	Play					

Concert Eb

Apply what you have learned from the Jazz Starters as you play the *Little Bees*
Jazz Ensemble Chart on pages 44 and 45 or **Lead Sheet** on page 56.

LITTLE BEES

Dean Sorenson

*To practice soloing on this chart, use the solo section accompaniment groove recording in your *Interactive Practice Studio*. The written solo is played the first time through.

Rollin' the Blues Away
Piano Spotlight

 Use the recordings and other features included in the *First Place for Jazz Interactive Practice Studio*. See page 1 for more details.

Exercise A will help you practice the basic rhythm section groove for the solo section of the *Rollin' the Blues Away*. When playing a basic groove, you are comping. Make certain to play with a firm touch on the keys and avoid the sustain pedal.

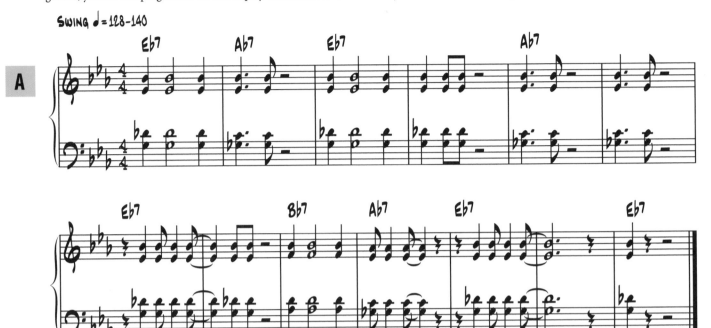

JAZZ THEORY **Comping** is the combination of chord voicings and improvised rhythms.

Exercise B will help you practice an extended "As Is" passage from the *Rollin' the Blues Away* jazz ensemble chart. Listen carefully to the recording and match it as closely as possible.

JAZZ THEORY The markings above the notes are called **articulations** and are commonly included in ensemble parts. They are included here since your part reinforces the ensemble. Play the notes marked ∧ short and accented and the notes marked > long and accented.

Concert E♭

☐ Check your progress on page 47 after each exercise.

LESSON 1 - Guitar and Vibes Play the Melody

Play the exercise, focusing on rhythm, tempo, and balance. Pay particular attention to the correct performance of articulation markings and play the chords with strong accents. Listen carefully to the recording and match it as closely as possible.

 The **shout chorus** is generally the loudest part of a chart. Play the marked dynamics but always listen for balance.

LESSON 2 - Drums Play Basic Figures

Play your part from Lesson 1, focusing on rhythm, tempo, and balance. Match the recording as closely as possible.

LESSON 3 - Drums Add Set-ups

Play your part from Lesson 1, focusing on rhythm, tempo, and balance. Match the recording as closely as possible.

LESSON 4 - Drums Play Fills, Figures, and Set-ups

Play your part from Lesson 1, focusing on rhythm, tempo, and balance. Match the recording as closely as possible.

Practice your part by using the **rhythm section practice track** for your instrument.

Concert E♭

W75P

E♭ Blues Scale

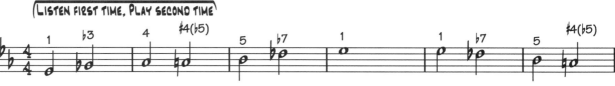

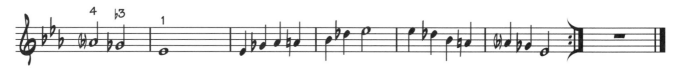

JAZZ THEORY *Rollin' the Blues Away* uses the E♭ **blues scale**. It is the same as the scale used for *Pink Flamingo Night* (pp.14-17) and *Chasing the Sun* (pp. 30-33), only now it is built on E♭. Remember, the blues scale differs from the major scale in several significant ways: 1) the third and seventh degrees are lowered one half step; 2) the second and sixth degrees are omitted; 3) a fifth degree lowered one half step is added (notated as #4 for ease of reading).

E♭ Blues Pitch Sets

After listening to and playing each Pitch Set as written, skip to **Improvisation Practice** and play a solo using only those scale degrees.

Use any scale degree. Write the scale degrees above the notes before you play.

Concert E♭

E♭ Blues Dominant Seventh Chords — E♭7, A♭7, B♭7

Write half note chord tones for **E♭7**, **A♭7**, and **B♭7** as indicated in the staff below.
There is no key signature, so don't forget to add accidentals.
Play the chord tones to hear the relationships.

JAZZ THEORY Like *Pink Flamingo Night* (pp. 14-17) and *Chasing the Sun* (pp. 30-33), *Rollin' the Blues Away* uses a blues progression comprised of three dominant seventh chords. This time the chords are built on E♭, A♭, and B♭ to create an **E♭ blues progression**. The chord symbols are **E♭7**, **A♭7**, and **B♭7**.

Accompaniment Grooves

Use this Accompaniment Groove for exercise **A** and **Improvisation Practice** .

Use this Accompaniment Groove for exercise **B** and **D** .

Improvisation Practice

Improvisation Practice takes you through the solo section of *Rollin' the Blues Away* two times. Even though the chords change, you can improvise over the entire solo section using pitches from the E♭ blues scale.

☑ Let's Check Progress

E♭ Blues

		Practiced		Mastered
A	Play			
B1	As Written			
	Improv Practice			
B2	As Written			
	Improv Practice			
B3	As Written			
	Improv Practice			
B4	As Written			
	Improv Practice			
C	Write			
	Play			

		Practiced		Mastered
Piano Spotlight	**A**			
	B			
Rhythm Sectional	**4**			

Apply what you have learned from the Jazz Starters as you play the *Rollin' the Blues Away*
Jazz Ensemble Chart on pages 48 and 49 or **Lead Sheet** on page 56B.

Concert E♭

Rollin' the Blues Away

Piano

Dean Sorenson

*To practice soloing on this chart, use the solo section accompaniment groove recording in your *Interactive Practice Studio*. The written solo is played the first time through.

Lead sheets provide the most common means of communication for jazz musicians. They present the music in its most basic form, usually including only the melody and chords, without articulations and dynamics that are commonly found in full arrangements. Using the *First Place for Jazz* lead sheets allows you to hone the skills learned in the Spotlights, Rhythm Sectionals, and Jazz Starters and gives you the chance to play the melody, even if you do not play it in the jazz ensemble charts.

Jazz musicians commonly play from lead sheets when performing in small group or combo settings. A jazz combo can include many different combinations of instruments, unlike the full jazz ensemble, which has a standard instrumentation. Jazz combos are typically constructed of two main elements:

> **rhythm section** – bass, drums, and piano; guitar may be included, sometimes substituting for piano. Auxiliary or mallet percussion may also be included.

> **front line** – any combination of winds, strings, mallet instruments, or vocalists. The front line can include anywhere from one to five performers.

The front line instruments play the melody while the rhythm section plays the accompaniment groove. Guitar or piano may also play the melody. In addition, jazz combos give all players many opportunities to improvise.

You can play the lead sheets on pages 50/51—56C as part of a combo with your band's rhythm section, or by using the lead sheet accompaniments found in the *First Place for Jazz Interactive Practice Studio*.

JUMPIN' JELLYBEANS

ROCK   In the **OPEN SOLO SECTION**, improvise using pitches from the Bb major scale (see page 2).   DEAN SORENSON

Jumpin' Jellybeans

Dean Sorenson

QUARTERBACK SNEAK

BOSSA In the **OPEN SOLO SECTION**, improvise using pitches from the B♭ Mixolydian scale (see page 6).   DEAN SORENSON

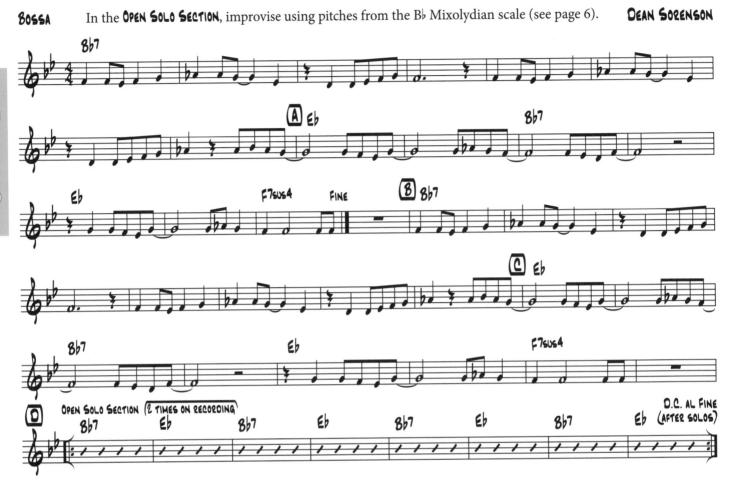

Quarterback Sneak

Dean Sorenson

Concert B♭

W75P

A Darker Shade of Gray

SWING   In the **Open Solo Section**, improvise using pitches from the Bb Dorian scale (see page 10).   Dean Sorenson

Concert Bb

A Darker Shade of Gray

PINK FLAMINGO NIGHT

ROCK   In the **OPEN SOLO SECTION**, improvise using pitches from the Bb blues scale (see page 14).   DEAN SORENSON

Concert Bb

Pink Flamingo Night

Dean Sorenson

SUMMER IN SÃO PAULO

BOSSA In the **OPEN SOLO SECTION**, improvise using pitches from the F major scale (see page 18). **DEAN SORENSON**

Concert F

Summer in São Paulo

Dean Sorenson

Concert F

THE LADY KNOWS HER CHEESE

SWING   In the **OPEN SOLO SECTION**, improvise using pitches from the F Mixolydian scale (see page 22).   DEAN SORENSON

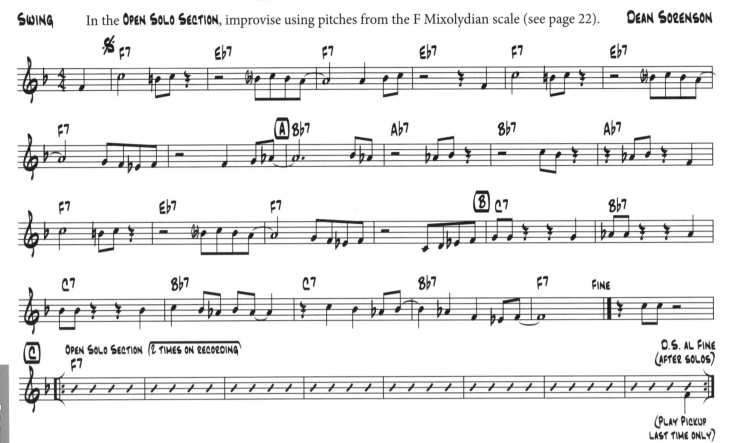

Concert F

The Lady Knows Her Cheese

Swing

Dean Sorenson

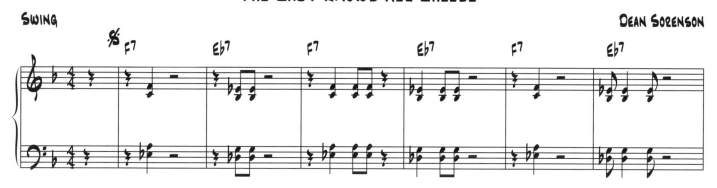

Concert F

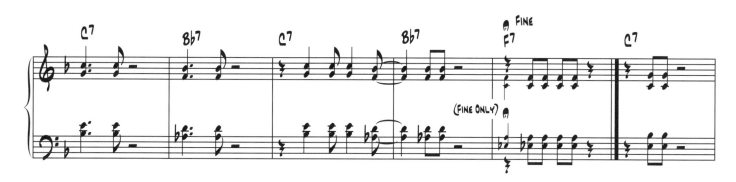

LUCKY SEVEN

Rock   In the OPEN SOLO SECTION, improvise using pitches from the F Dorian scale (see page 26).

DEAN SORENSON

Concert F

LUCKY SEVEN

Rock

Dean Sorenson

Concert F

CHASING THE SUN

SALSA In the **OPEN SOLO SECTION**, improvise using pitches from the F blues scale (see page 30). **DEAN SORENSON**

Concert F

Chasing the Sun

Salsa

Dean Sorenson

Concert F

EVENING STROLL

SWING   In the **OPEN SOLO SECTION**, improvise using pitches from the E♭ major scale (see page 34).   DEAN SORENSON

Concert E♭

Evening Stroll

CRUTCH NOT MUCH

ROCK　　　In the **OPEN SOLO SECTION**, improvise using pitches from the E♭ Mixolydian scale (see page 38).　　　DEAN SORENSON

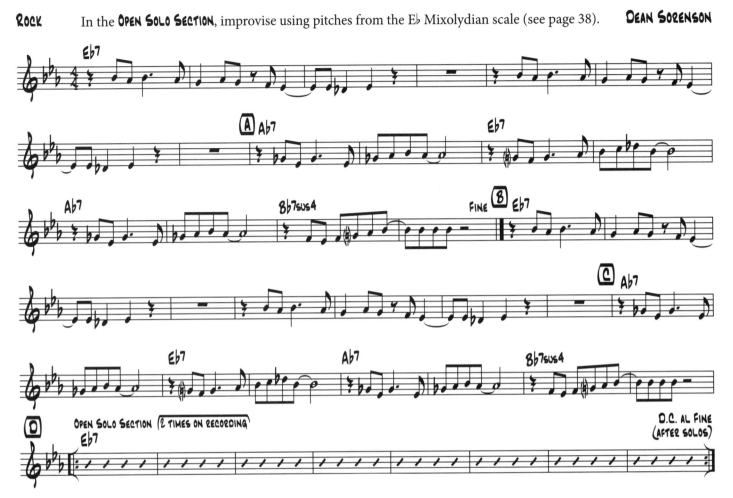

CRUTCH NOT MUCH

Rock

Dean Sorenson

(Bass clef part optional)

Concert E♭

W75P

Little Bees

Bossa   In the **Open Solo Section**, improvise using pitches from the E♭ Dorian scale (see page 42).   Dean Sorenson

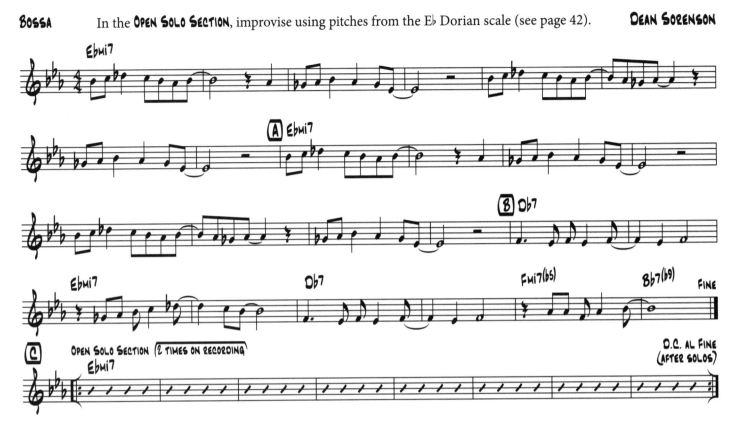

Little Bees

Bossa

Dean Sorenson

Rollin' the Blues Away

SWING — In the **OPEN SOLO SECTION**, improvise using pitches from the Eb blues scale (see page 46).

DEAN SORENSON

ACCOMPANIMENT GROOVES

Rollin' the Blues Away

SWING

DEAN SORENSON

W75P